USBORNE
Write Your Own
POEMS

With poems by

....

....

Contents

4 Getting started

What do poems look and sound like?

8 Ridiculous rhymes

9 Ludicrous limericks

10 A is for Alphabet

12 Short and sharp: haikus

14 The shape of a poem

16 Sonnets

18 Try a triolet

20 The perplexing pantoum

22 Invent your own form

24 Poetical comparisons

26 What am I?

28 Ask, argue, command

30 Choose an imaginary reader

32 The luck of the draw

What are poems about?

36 Who are you?

38 Peculiar self-portraits

40 Who might you be?

42 Animal, vegetable, mineral?

44 The great outdoors

46 Eyes closed, mind open

47 Dawn and dusk

48 A poem is a time machine

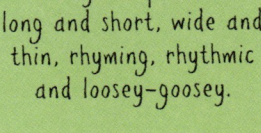

Try out poems long and short, wide and thin, rhyming, rhythmic and loosey-goosey.

Write poems with repeated lines and tricky rhymes

Discover the ancient art of riddles

Add zip, zing and zest to your poems

Pretend you're someone – or something – else

50   An ode to something great or small

52   The call of the wild

54   Making art out of art

56   A map to unseen worlds

58   Don't make a long story short

Write ferocious, fantastical animal poems

Write poems on an epic scale

Pushing the boundaries

64   Stop making sense

66   Erasing a poem

68   Snip, rip, copy, glue

70   Poems off the page

71   Chance operations

72   Poetry out loud

74   Straight outta Greenland

76   Team efforts

78   Get in line

Write a poem with a pair of scissors

Write a poem with a pack of cards

Find definitions and explanations of poetry words

Toolkit

82   What is poetry?

84   What makes a poem a poem?

86   Tantalizing titles

88   Revise, revise, revise

90   Invent a secret identity

92   Everyday tips for poets

94   Poetry first aid

95   Emergency measures

Usborne Quicklinks

For links to websites where you can listen to and read the poems mentioned in this book, and find more tips and inspiration to help you write your own poems, go to the Usborne Quicklinks website at www.usborne.com/quicklinks and enter the keywords 'write your own poems'.

Please follow the online safety guidelines at the Usborne Quicklinks website. Children should be supervised online.

Getting started

Anyone can be a poet. All you need to write poems... is YOU. That's really what poems are made of:

Your thoughts

Your words

Your ideas

Your feelings

Your voice

Oh – there are just a couple more things that might help along the way...

A dash of daring

You'll learn lots of different rules for poems in this book – but you don't have to follow them.

Lots of great poems are made when poets *break the rules*.

An open mind

This book will encourage you to experiment with writing ALL KINDS of poems: old and new, serious and silly.

As you go through this book, look out for...

...lots of "More to read" boxes, so you can discover amazing poems.

...suggestions, challenges and tricks to kick-start new writing projects.

...helpful lists of words, rhymes, titles and things to write about.

More to read

"I Started Early – Took my Dog"
by Emily Dickinson

"The Look"
by Carol Ann Duffy

You can easily find these poems in a library, or by clicking on the links provided at the Usborne Quicklinks website.

If some poems seem hard or confusing at first, don't worry.

That's normal – and it's ok to enjoy **reading** and **writing** poems without understanding precisely what every word or line means.

Sketch

Jot

Scribble

Note

VERSIFY

scratch

Off you go!

Turn the page to dive right in and start writing poems. At the back of the book, in the **Toolkit** section, you'll find useful definitions and suggestions in case you ever get stuck.

What do poems look and sound like?

Poems can be *all kinds* of things. They can be long or short, wide or thin. They can be rhyming and rhythmic, or sound like an ordinary conversation.

In this section, you can try out many different styles of poems – and even make up new forms that no one has ever seen or heard before.

Ridiculous rhymes

One of the tools poets use to give poems a special sound and feel is rhymes – words that end in the same, or nearly the same, sound. Your poems don't have to rhyme, but it can be a lot of fun thinking up amusing rhymes.

Try adding some more rhymes to these examples. Do any of them give you ideas for a new poem?

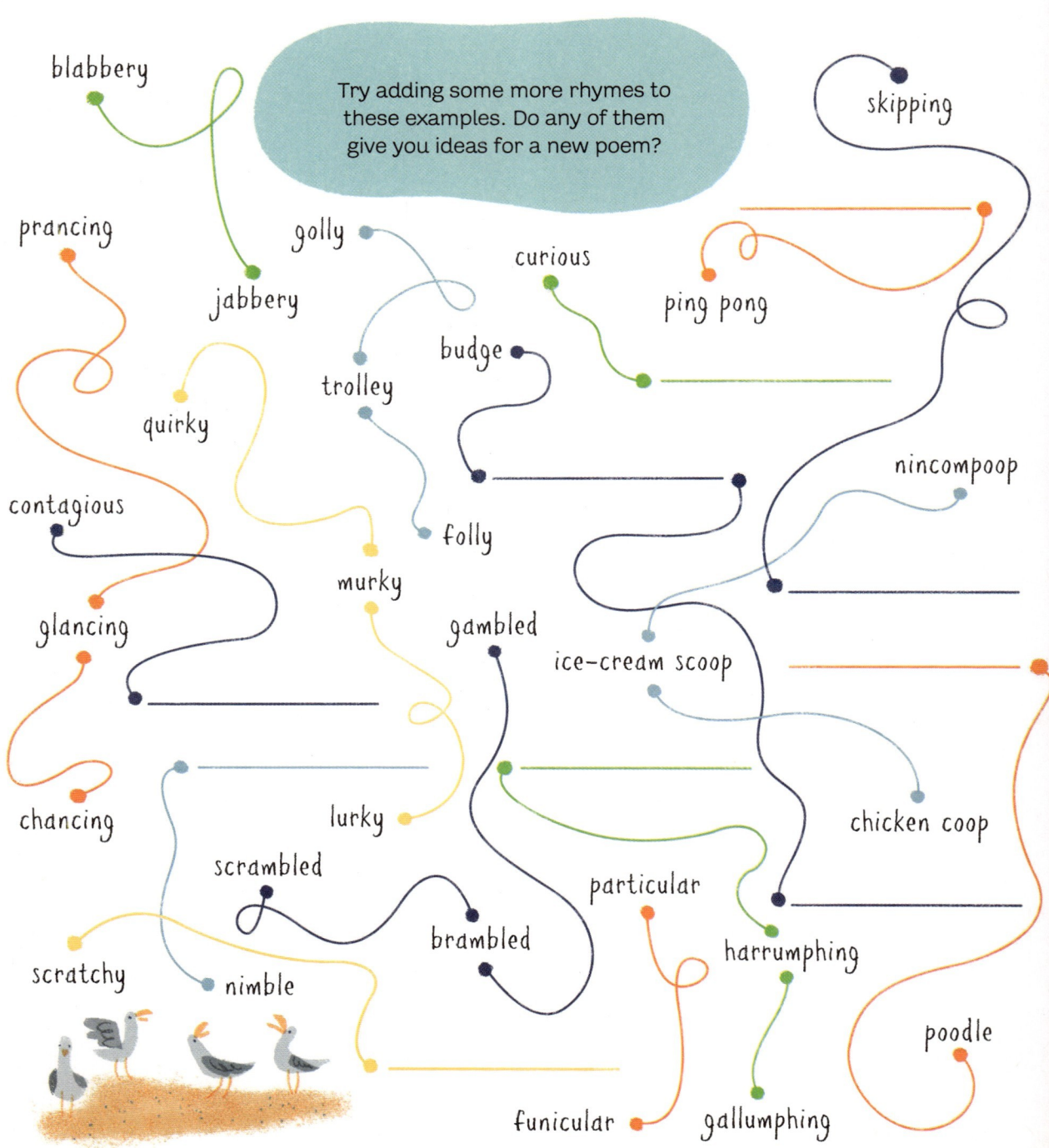

blabbery

skipping

prancing

golly

curious

jabbery

ping pong

budge

trolley

quirky

nincompoop

contagious

folly

murky

glancing

gambled

ice-cream scoop

chancing

lurky

chicken coop

scrambled

particular

brambled

harrumphing

scratchy

nimble

poodle

funicular

gallumphing

Ludicrous limericks

One kind of rhyming poem with a rollicking rhythm is called a limerick. Limericks usually give a silly, bizarre description of an imaginary person. Often, that person's home town or country is mentioned in the first line.

The poet from Crewe

There was a young poet from Crewe
who slowly composed a haiku:
he wrote his first line
at a quarter to nine
and he finished aged seventy-two.

Note: A haiku is a very short poem.

To write one, turn to page 10.

The balloonist

There once was an old man from Spain
too frightened to travel by plane;
he tied some balloons
to his blue pantaloons
and floated from Cádiz to Maine.

Limericks are usually five lines long.

Write your own limerick here:

More to read

"A young lady of Lynn" by Anonymous

"How awkward when playing with glue" by Constance Levy

A is for alphabet

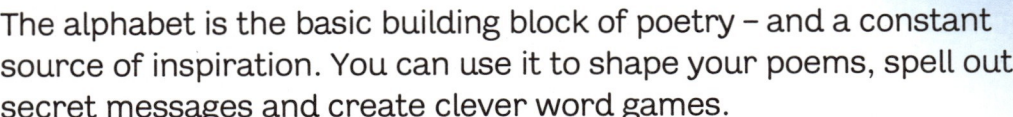

The alphabet is the basic building block of poetry – and a constant source of inspiration. You can use it to shape your poems, spell out secret messages and create clever word games.

Orderly abecedarians

Challenge yourself to write a poem in which the first letter of each new line follows the order of the alphabet. This is called an **abecedarian**.

An abecedarian could be about the alphabet:

A is for Alpinist
        scaling the peaks
B is for Botanist
        studying leeks
C is for Cyclist
        whose bicycle squeaks...

Or it needn't refer to the alphabet at all:

An avalanche
        was roaring by
But stopped
        itself to say,
"Could you please help?
        I've come from UP –
Does DOWN
        go past this way?"

More to read

"Abecedary"
by Tom Disch

"Alphabet Poem"
by Edward Lear

A ....
B ....
C ....
D ....
E ....
F ....
G ....
H ....
I ....
J ....
K ....
L ....
M ....
N ....
O ....
P ....
Q ....
R ....
S ....
T ....
U ....
V ....
W ....
X ....
Y ....
Z ....

Crafty acrostics

In **acrostic** poems, the first letters of each line spell out words or names. Write an acrostic here based on your name or the name of someone you know. It could rhyme, but it doesn't have to.

A secret might not be
C oncealed. It could lie
R ight before your eyes:
O ut in the open,
S aid without speaking,
T old to whoever
I s able to spot it
C apering down the page.

Wonderful word squares

Here's an alphabet-based poetry game to try. It's a **word square**: a grid of letters that can be read both across and down. These are tricky to compose – and the more letters you use, and the bigger the square, the more difficult it is.

B	A	R	E
A	W	A	Y
R	A	R	E
E	Y	E	S

P	L	O	D
L	O	P	E
O	P	E	N
D	E	N	T

Short and sharp: haikus

Not all poems have to rhyme. Haikus are very short, non-rhyming poems. They were invented hundreds of years ago in Japan, and are still written today.

A haiku is usually three lines long.

*This late summer night
the narrow new moon swims up:
an octopus eye.*

Its first line has five syllables, the second has seven syllables, and the third has five – making a total of 17 syllables.

Haikus traditionally include at least one word or phrase that refers to a season or time of year. This part of the haiku is known as a kigo.

*Snow deepens outside.
Sleepy student, wakeful mouse –
both nibble their books.*

In this haiku, "snow deepens" is a kigo. It shows that the poem takes place in the wintertime.

You could use some of these kigos in your poems.

SPRING WORDS

Foals

Flooding streams

Mud

Daffodils

Thawing ice

Sparrows twittering

Green buds

Bluebells

Racing lambs

FLYING KITES

Cherry blossoms

Spring rain

SUMMERY WORDS

Watermelons

short nights

FIREWORKS

Bare feet

Cicadas

THUNDERSTORMS

Billowing clouds

Mosquitos

Hot afternoons

Mowing grass

Sunflowers

SHADY TREES

Swimming pools

Write your own haikus here:

AUTUMNAL WORDS

Mist

Migrating geese

Falling chestnuts

HAYSTACKS

Bonfires

Mushroom gathering

Harvest moon

Lamplight

CRISP AIR

LINGERING DUSK

Spiderwebs

Pumpkins

Red and yellow leaves

WINTERY WORDS

Bare branches

Lost mittens

Holly leaves

ICICLES

FROZEN STREAMS

Withered fields

Gingerbread

Runny noses

Fresh snow

Fireplace

Frosted windows

Ice skates

Blizzard

The shape of a poem

Most poems have a tall, narrow, boxy shape, with one line simply stacked on top of another. But you can also arrange the words of your poem to create a pattern, shape or picture. Poems that do this are called **concrete**, or **shape poems**.

This shape poem is made from three groups of text that can be read in any order.

Parts of a dragonfly

I waver like the see-through outer edge of cyclones, or the air above the body of a flame, or breath before a panting four-horse team that draws the golden carriage of the Sun.

One twin among two fanning pairs.
I am as pale as the water a fishscale shines through – thin as the film on summer sleep.

Think of me as the diamond-green and oil-dipped pin securing the double hinge of flight.

I neither flit nor flutter: still at the start of a million ripples. I am the sink ing stone.

The dragonfly's legs are made using punctuation marks.

A poem without a shape

Some poems don't have regular **rhymes**, or repeating **rhythms**, or counted **syllables** – or even breaks between lines. They are simply blocks of text, which take the shape of the page they're written on. They look just like **prose** – the kind of writing you might find in a newspaper, a novel, or an instruction manual – and they are called **prose poems**.

What makes a prose poem a poem? It may just be down to a poetical choice of words and ideas.

Use this space to create a shape poem – or a prose poem – of your own:

Tips for shape poems

To start, use a pencil to draw a faint outline of the shape of your poem.

Use a pen to fill in the shape with your words.

Erase the pencil lines, leaving behind your finished poem.

More to read

Shape poems

"Christmas Tree" by James Merrill

"Swan and Shadow" by John Hollander

Prose poems

"Bath" by Amy Lowell

"The Fox" by Khalil Gibran

Sonnets

The structure of a poem – its rhymes and repetitions, and the way the words are set out – is known as its **form**. There are lots of different forms, including one called a sonnet.

A Shakespearean sonnet

You can write a sonnet lots of different ways – with different patterns of rhymes or no rhymes at all – but sonnets *usually* have fourteen lines.

This sample poem is made up of three groups of four lines, each with alternating rhymes, followed by a **rhyming couplet**: a pair of lines that rhyme with each other. This style of sonnet was made famous by **William Shakespeare**.

The rhyming patterns used in poems are called **rhyme schemes**.

They are often mapped out with letters. Each new letter marks a new and different rhyming sound.

The rhythm used in Shakespearean sonnets is **iambic**, which means the lines each sound something like this:

da DUM, da DUM, da DUM, da DUM, da DUM

See page 85 for more about rhythm.

A fly's to-do list

Rhymes:

I must, before this day comes to a close,   a
leave undetected footprints in the jam,   b
touch down repeatedly on someone's nose,   a
and dart off from the brushing of a hand.   b

I must contaminate some breakfast crumbs,   c
patrol a weaving course I can't unwind,   d
and, dazzled by a sunbeam, I must drum   c
between the shining window and the blind.   d

I must submerge in coffee cups, and swill   e
the spattered edges of a plate, and scale   f
the walls, and flit, and stop, and stare, and fill   e
my big red eyes with light before it fails...   f

Before the night falls – or the swatter does –   g
I'll buzz and buzz and buzz and buzz and buzz.   g

Note: Good rhymes don't have to be perfect. Rhymes that sound just a little off – like jam and hand – are called **slant rhymes**.

AVON JAMS

You could write your own sonnet here:

More to read

"Autumn Birds"
by John Clare

"Wood Not Yet Out"
by Alice Oswald

"Pied Beauty"
by Gerard Manley
Hopkins

Try a triolet

Over 500 years ago, in medieval times, French poets invented something called a **triolet** (TREE-oh-lay). It is only eight lines long, but it has a tricky pattern of rhymes and exactly (or *almost* exactly) repeated lines.

Repetitions:

Lucky Duck

Rhymes:

Not to love a duck is hard.	a
They paddle for the luck they get.	b
They jostle, pirouette and barge,	a
but not to love a duck is hard.	a
How greedily they race toward	a
a crust – a crumb – a speck! And yet	b
you can't not love a duck. It's hard:	a
they paddle for the luck they get.	b

The rhyme scheme for this poem has just two rhyming sounds: a (rhymes with hard) and b (rhymes with get).

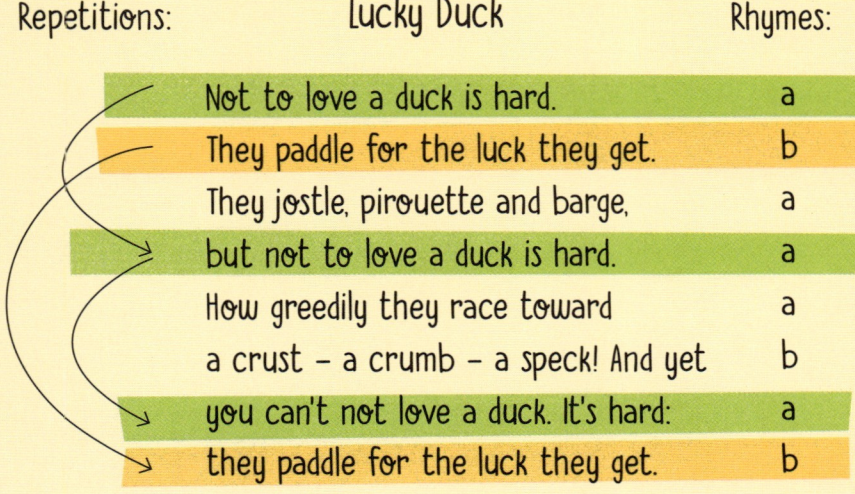

Try filling in the blanks to complete this triolet:

Title: _____

I wonder, have you ever tried	a
A pepper-pickled apricot?	b
	a
	a
	a
	b
	a
	b

Remember to repeat the two opening lines!

More to read

"Birds at Winter Nightfall" by Thomas Hardy

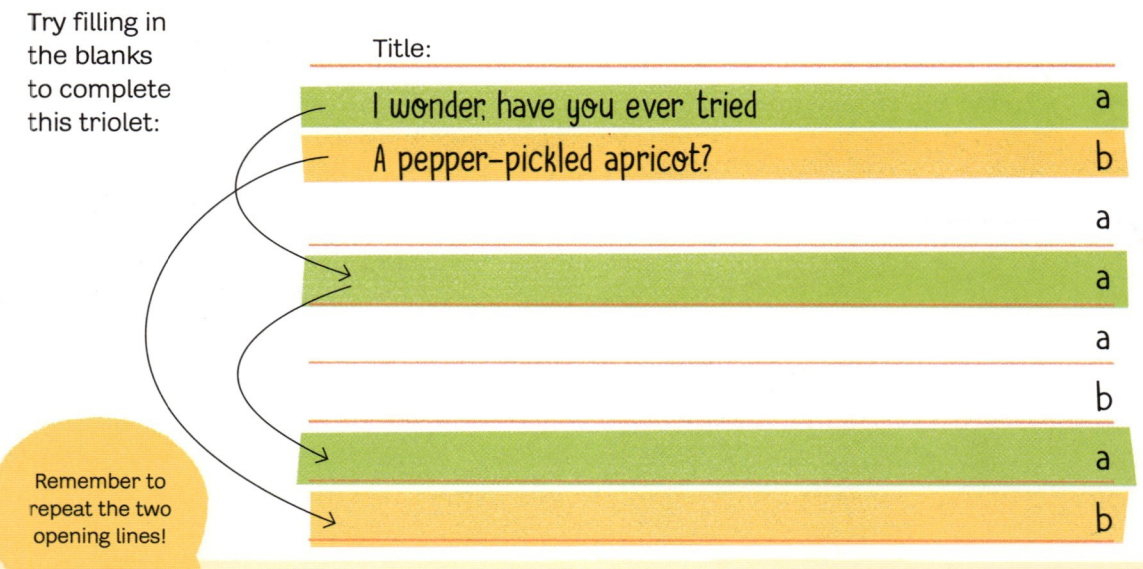

Write your own triolet here:

Help! Rhymes are hard

Yes, they are. Here are a few helpful tips:

- Start planning your rhymes before you write all the way to the end of a line.

- Your first rhyme may not be your best. Try to list every possible rhyming word for a particular line before choosing one.

- Let the rhymes lead you. Sometimes it's ok to be guided by the sheer luck of a clever rhyme. It might send your poem swerving off course – but that's half the fun!

The perplexing pantoum

On this page, you'll find another type of poem, called a **pantoum**, that doesn't have to rhyme. Like many other poems, it is divided into separate groups of lines called **stanzas**. In a pantoum, these stanzas are all linked together by a pattern of repeating lines.

Lines 2 and 4 of one stanza become lines 1 and 3 in the next. Each line should appear twice in your pantoum. The first line is often also the last.

This sample poem is divided into four stanzas.

Stellar Probe XX0811

1. Through million-light-year cavities of space
2. I race along a non-returning curve
3. I can't recall the start of.
4. Bursts of radiation char my data banks.

2. I race along a non-returning curve,
5. Among steep-sided quasars, wayward planets,
4. Bursts of radiation... Charred-out data banks
6. And un-updated systems flicker, tick, record:

5. Steep-sided quasars, wayward planets
7. Looping through their nebulas...
6. My un-updated systems flicker, tick, record,
8. And beam this back to somewhere I've forgotten.

7. Looping through some nebula
3. I can't recall the start of,
8. Still I beam this back to somewhere I've forgotten –
1. Through the million-light-year cavities of space.

The pantoum has its origins in poetry from Malaysia.

Write your own pantoum by filling in these blanks with pairs of lines. (Remember that you don't have to repeat each of your lines *exactly*.) You could write about anything – for example, an explorer's letter home from a distant planet, or a recipe for a magic potion.

More to read
"Pantoum"
by Sandra Lim

Title:

Invent your own form

Poetic forms are like recipes for writing: they suggest ingredients, rules and processes that produce a certain kind of poem.

There are hundreds of poetic forms in use today – including limericks and pantoums – and many have been around for centuries.

But there's no reason why you can't create something completely new. Use these pages to write poems in your very own shape and style.

You could combine two or three of these elements:

- A pattern of rhymes
- A series of repeated lines
- A pattern of varying line lengths
- A fixed number of syllables per line
- A particular rhythm (da-da-DUM da-da-DUM)
- A particular outline or shape (triangle, circle, zig-zag)

Once you've created your own poetic form...

- Give it a name.
- Write several poems using this form.
- Share your poems with other people. Your brand new form just might catch on.

Poetical comparisons

To write poetry, you need to be a good observer – and you need a vivid imagination. This is especially true when it comes to making poetical comparisons called **similes** and **metaphors**.

Similes

A simile uses the words **as** or **like** to compare two different things. People often use similes in everyday speech:

Arthur is <u>as</u> sharp <u>as</u> a tack.

Henry is <u>as</u> cool <u>as</u> a cucumber.

Camille slept <u>like</u> a log.

To make things interesting, try finding similarities between objects that wouldn't usually be brought together – for example, an iceberg and a tiger, as in this poem.

The iceberg's tall and sunlit side
was glossy <u>as</u> a tiger's pelt –
but, <u>like</u> the tiger's stripy hide,
when it was touched, its teeth were felt.

Fill in the blanks to create your own similes here:

A sinking ship is like _____

A sleeping cat is like _____

A crown is like _____

The stars were as _____ as _____

My nose is as _____ as _____

Your voice is as _____ as _____

Metaphors

A metaphor is a way of describing something by comparing it with something else. But metaphors don't bother with **as** or **like**. They describe one thing as if it were something else, and trust a reader to make sense of it.

What's the difference?

Simile: **X is like Y**

Metaphor: **X *is* Y**

Here are some common, everyday metaphors:

Alex is a bit prickly today.
Alice is a couch potato.
It's a jungle out there!

This poem uses metaphor to compare icebergs to a tiger's teeth.

The bay with jagged icebergs gleamed.
We looked. We paused.
We sailed into the tiger's jaws.

No one is literally sailing into a tiger's mouth. The poem suggests that the bay full of icebergs *is like* a tiger's mouth full of deadly teeth.

Saying it in the form of a metaphor makes it feel more dangerous, dramatic and real.

Book *Bed* Drum
City *Honey* *Magpie*
Brook Seed **Elephant**
ANGEL Canyon *Yacht*
Gold Tent *Valentine*
Butter *Ear* Pine *Rose*
Ambulance
Comet *Globe* Axes
December **Coal**

Make metaphors by combining two things from this list. What similarities link them? Could a word commonly used to describe one thing also describe the other?

The *ambulance* sped off, a hot *coal* winking in the night.

_____

_____

_____

_____

_____

What am I?

Poems aren't always easy to understand, but that can be part of what makes them interesting. This is particularly true for **riddles** – poems that describe a specific subject using a series of misleading and confusing clues.

Riddles often disguise their subject using **metaphors.** (See page 25)

I've twice as many horns as feet;
I hurry, but I'm never fleet.
I'm never homeless, never hatless;
I carry a globe, but never an atlas.
You'll find me on a silver trail
among the carrots, peas and kale.

Do you think the subject of this riddle carries an actual globe? Or just something *like* a globe?

Many riddles contain a **paradox** – a statement that might appear true or logical, but which contradicts itself.

I hold no treasure,
hide no vault,
and cause no grief.
Whoever chops
me open sees,
through flowing tears,
my rows of arches
and my troves of rings.

How is it possible for something to cause tears, but not grief – or to have rings, but no treasure? Solving the paradox solves the riddle.

Answers:
a snail, an onion

Write some "What am I?" riddles of your own. You could choose subjects from everyday life that would be familiar to most people, but which you can disguise in your descriptions.

Remember that a good riddle is hard, but not impossible, to solve.

How to write a riddle

First choose a subject: a famous person, an animal, a food, a household object. Then, as in this example, write words you associate with the subject or might use to describe it. You can use those as the basis of your riddle.

Has just one foot

Moves slowly

Leaves a trail

Glistening

Snail

Lives in its shell

Silver

Never homeless

Round like a globe

Likes to eat vegetables and leaves

Ask, argue, command

There are lots of different kinds of speech you can use in your poems to influence, move and persuade your readers.

Depending on what you want your poem to do, you may want to...

Flatter
No sponge is deeper,
nor so light;
no butter-cream
so densely white...

Ask
Where are the cakes
of birthdays past?
Do piped rosettes
all fade so fast?

Argue
The queen of all
the cakes and pies
is carrot cake.
I'll tell you why...

Command
Stop. Sit. Eat.
I've made this nice
banana walnut
toffee slice.

Boast
No fancy French
patisserie
can claim a chef
as fine as me!

Apologize
Crooked piping,
runny jam –
I should have tried
to make a flan...

Pray
Please, let this bowl
of lumpy gunge
become four tiers
of stately sponge.

Exclaim
A cake! A cake!
Oh! Let me taste
a bite – a slice –
a heaping plate!

Dialogue
"What is this tartly
sweet confection?"
"A lemon drizzle
cake: perfection."

Define
An angel cake
is sponge so light
if left uneaten
it takes flight.

Curse
May thunder roll
and lightning come
and strike whoever
steals a crumb.

Choose four of the different ways of speaking from the opposite page. List them here, and then use them all in a poem with the title **Invitation to a party**.

1.

2.

3.

4.

Choose an imaginary reader

When you write a poem, it can help to think about who might read it. How do you adjust your language and tone of voice to suit different readers?

On these pages, try writing the same poem – either about your most treasured possession or your best friend – five times. Each time, revise it to fit completely different situations and readers.

What kind of words should you use – short? long? slangy? What should your tone of voice be – silly? warm? polite?

How would you write your poem if it were...

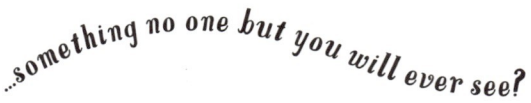

...something no one but you will ever see?

....

....

....

....

....

....

....

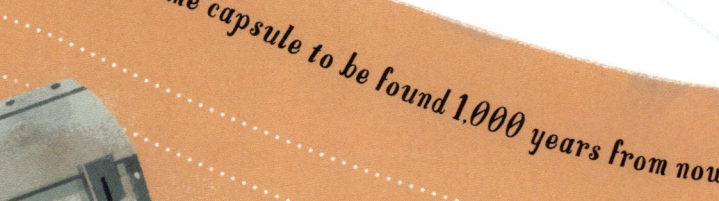

...hidden in a time capsule to be found 1,000 years from now?

...nailed to the door
of your deadliest foe?

...carved on a public monument?

...a message in a bottle, set adrift on the ocean?

The luck of the draw

It's easy to fall into the trap of using the same words over and over again. Refreshing your vocabulary can add a bit of zing – and can give you new and unexpected ideas for poems.

Write down the first nine words you find in this word search. Then use them to write a poem on the opposite page.

```
                        T D N I
              Z       C   A   B
      B   T E M   Y A Y E R
      R W M   Y A Y E R F
          X S I E X C T S T
          X M M F P G C K H P Y
          V H A R N E S S E M A O B
          U P N A Q R O W E L A N H L
          Z O C M E R M A I D L I D R E
        D I M P L E D A U F P Y A L H D G
        B E X C P O Q R N K M E R R O R E N
      B   O C Z Q E U H F G Q F S F C O R X S A
        M A T T E R D G J A N U P C L A M B E R B
        F E F T M D L E A R R O W M V A E B L R W L E
        X R K J L A L P D Q E C A C Z P P R I S M E I S J
      W B O K S F W B S Z Q S A P T C J I B U Z L G G X U
      N D A J B E C L T M O U C D I H G U L F N M Y S H I R E
      C E B P E R U V I A N E U E L O N M V J A E V O T F E S
      N Y T D N T G P M V E E R G A M B E R G R I S E C N A O
      N C H R W M Y E N F N G C R H H O E J F U M H R X D T M
      C A A J O R B D C L L D I E H U N D R E D B N I E F U R
      I Q G U O E E I Y Y A Q M H O N M C A I L U T H Z X R A
      N N G L A Z E D F C O M X J U P M D P W E L P D V X K W
      A V O L E R V U C R I S P L Y E U R O R H T B C R O N Y R
      F I Z Z E S I R I X T E R M I T E N T D T U M G X W U D N A
    W N E X R P D Y S A N O C R U X K K U Y A L A R M L E S S G R O
    I T N R I U P Q E E F E T Z Y M V E S U V I A N I X I P O L L E N
    L O A F I A K V I Q U T K W X S P R Y Q K O V U P A N T L E R S H
    B A O B A B L A N M T L E K J H U L A I J H W U G E E I T C H X P X
    V Y A L S A I L N I L T R L E J R E B G L O O P E R C D E V O U R
    Q O A E Q Z E E Y F C L E C C Y J L B J M V Z A R R C O R F E O P
    U L C T R O N I Z R U K J R B W A X A S A M X X S X F L E E T X
    K U A G I H K H E P O K D P K Y R W C O N T R A B A N D J J T
    R R A B B L E D C G Q X N K A N V L K U J E R G X A O C A R
    I P S E L F I E H Y T W A Z T T P X R E N H U I M M H U
    L Y L N E E D L E S S L Y C D T L U R N N C A L L A R
    M E P M M U E V C J U O D K X E F T C I H R E R D
    E T H E R F L U N W B D O L D R U M S E O I S
      Q X E R Y D X O U J B L U N D E R W A
      D Q A N R M U C X O X P J A P E
      R T J U N I P E R E X A
      D W A S P
```

Your words:

1. _____   4. _____   7. _____

2. _____   5. _____   8. _____

3. _____   6. _____   9. _____

Vibrant vocab

One good way to keep bringing new words into your vocabulary is to make a word list in a special notebook. Whenever you come across a particularly interesting word, add it to your notebook.

You can use your word list just like a painter uses a palette. Mix the words into surprising combinations and add them to your poem wherever they work best.

A really weird combination might send you in a new direction altogether.

rendezvous

queenly

alarm

gloop

devour

harum-scarum

doldrums

What are poems about?

Do poems have to be about real life? Should they tell a story? Can a painting inspire a poem?

In this section, you can write about the person you are and the people you aren't. You can describe the feeling of a sunny day outdoors and spin epic tales of make-believe.

Who are you?

Thinking about what makes you YOU is something you can do in a poem. Your poems can be self-portraits, describing your features, thoughts, ideas and experiences.

What eight words sum up your personality, or who you are on the inside?

Write an eight-word self-portrait that would help anyone – even a stranger – to spot you in a crowd.

Describe your bedroom in five lines. Is it tidy? Messy? A place you go to get away from other people, or a space you share? Do you have your best ideas there? What does it say about who you are?

How do the things you do sum up who you are? Try creating a self-portrait just by listing everything you did during one ordinary day last week. Where did you go? Who did you meet? What did you see?

Did you...
jog
amble
STRIDE
lumber
lounge
FLOP?

Did you...
chatter
negotiate
offer
pronounce
discuss
command?

Did you...
lunch
munch
gorge
snack
nibble
banquet?

Did you...
ponder
PLOT
DAYDREAM
fret
recall
forget?

Peculiar self-portraits

How do you see yourself? Does your personality change when you're dressed up as someone else? Or if you wake up in the middle of the night? Or when you're feeling unwell? Choose a title from the list below and use it as a starting point for a poem.

Self-portrait at 3 a.m.

Self-portrait on New Year's Day

Self-portrait in an astronaut's helmet

Self-portrait with flamingo legs

Self-portrait on my 110th birthday

Self-portrait with a mouth full of marshmallows

Self-portrait in a diving mask

Self-portrait in a rippling pond

Self-portrait with a soaring fever

Self-portrait in a teaspoon

Title:

Write the story of your life – in reverse. Start with today, and finish with the day you were born. You could also use some of the words you used to describe yourself on page 36.

Ideas for things to include:

- Your hobbies and interests
- New friends you've made
- Places you've been to
- Your fondest memory
- Your saddest day

More to read:

"Fifth Grade Autobiography" by Rita Dove

"A Girl Named Jack" by Jacqueline Woodson

Who might you be?

Writing a poem can be like putting on a mask. You can become whoever you want, and write from that person's point of view. This kind of poem is called a **persona poem**, or **dramatic monologue**.

Write a persona poem, perhaps based on one of the characters on these pages. Put yourself in their shoes – or sandals. How might they talk? What have they experienced?

A Polynesian voyager on a sea-going canoe

An elderly cat burglar

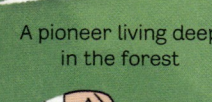

A pioneer living deep in the forest

An orphan on the streets of Victorian London

A poem without a hero

The person in your poem doesn't need to be great, good or even likable. Sometimes it's more interesting to write about a villain.

Your poem could show why someone commits wicked acts, and what he or she thinks and says afterwards...

A Roman gladiator

Think about who the person in your poem is talking to. Is it...

- A modern reader?

- A friend or relative?

- A stranger?

- A supernatural being?

- A helpless ant?

More to read

"Mummy of a Lady Named Jemutesonekh" by Thomas James

"Crusoe in England" by Elizabeth Bishop

A scientist who's made a shocking discovery

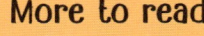

Animal, vegetable, mineral?

Try writing a persona poem (see page 40) as though you are an animal... or even an object. Use the suggestions here, or choose something else that sparks your imagination.

You could be...

- A giant squid from the depths of the ocean
- A picture frame holding a famous painting
- A goldsmith's hammer
- A space probe crashed on a distant planet
- A dung beetle rolling its ball of dung
- A cracked teacup
- A storm cloud
- The last living dodo
- A captive jaguar on a golden chain

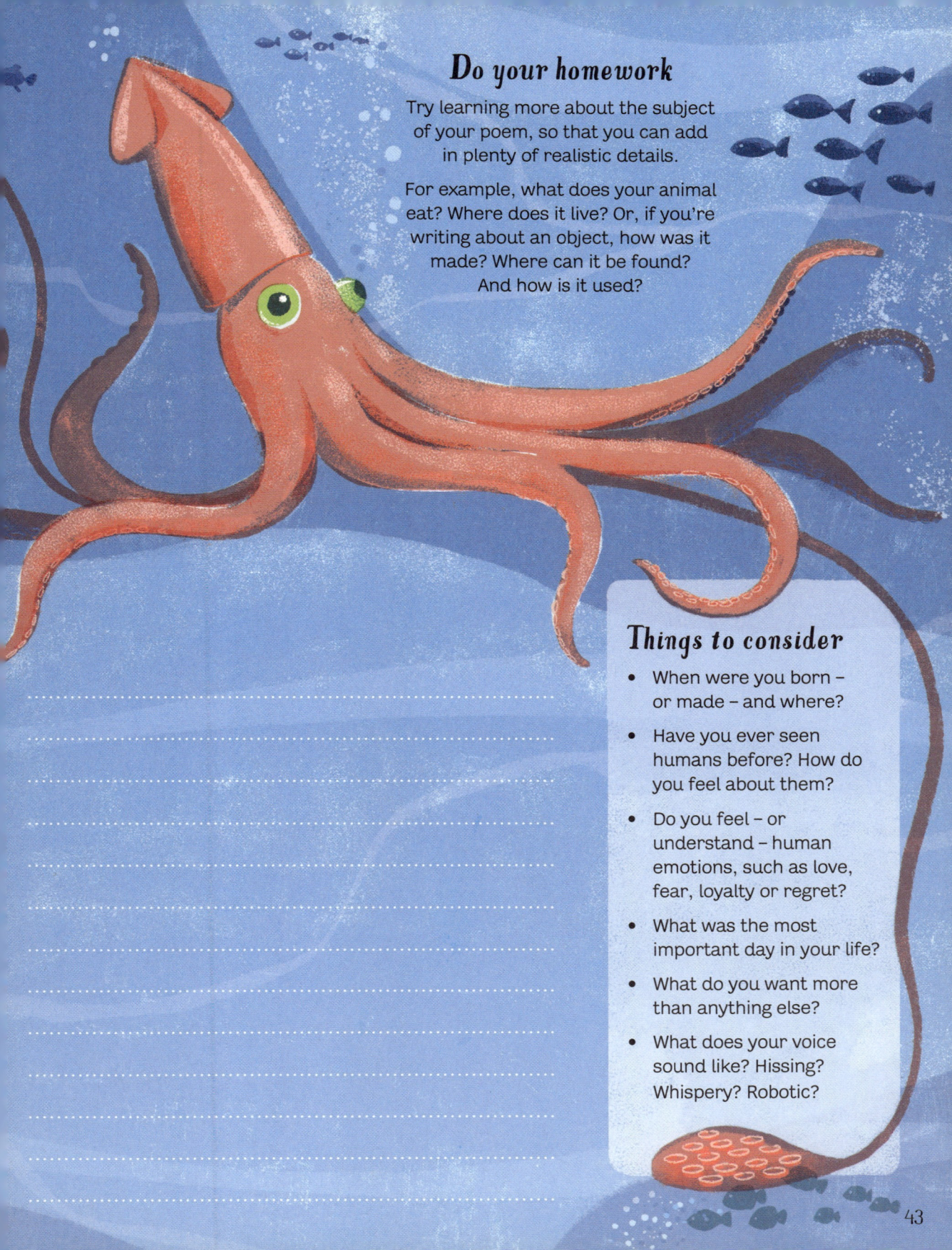

Do your homework

Try learning more about the subject of your poem, so that you can add in plenty of realistic details.

For example, what does your animal eat? Where does it live? Or, if you're writing about an object, how was it made? Where can it be found? And how is it used?

Things to consider

- When were you born – or made – and where?

- Have you ever seen humans before? How do you feel about them?

- Do you feel – or understand – human emotions, such as love, fear, loyalty or regret?

- What was the most important day in your life?

- What do you want more than anything else?

- What does your voice sound like? Hissing? Whispery? Robotic?

The great outdoors

Poems can make you feel a summer breeze on a snowy night, or conjure up a stormy sea when you're safely on dry land. To achieve this, you'll need to use your five senses – sight, hearing, smell, touch and taste – and ALL your powers of description.

On the following pages, you'll find some things to try the next time you're out in nature – in a forest, at the seaside, or in a park.

From far to near

Describe your surroundings – starting as far as you can see into the distance. What's on the horizon? What's just within hearing? Line by line, move nearer and nearer to where you are. What can you see just beyond your reach? What's under your feet?

Get your hands dirty

If you're actually outdoors, reach out and grab a handful of earth, or pebbles from a stream, or pine needles from the forest floor – whatever natural objects you can find. Write a short poem describing what you're holding: where it came from, what it looks, feels and smells like.

feathery
bristling
webbed
clustered
dazzling
gnarled
crackling
gurgling
soggy
clearing
wispy
gleaming
floating
shimmering
shady
budding
rattling
reflecting
raked
brittle
golden
overlapping
worn

More to read

"Sleeping in the Forest" by Mary Oliver

"the earth is a living thing" by Lucille Clifton

"Plea to the Wind" by Alice Oswald

"Blackberrying" by Sylvia Plath

Eyes closed, mind open

When you describe a place or a landscape, try not to rely only on what you see. Instead, find a safe place to sit, close your eyes and *listen*. Make a mental note of what you can hear around you – then, open your eyes again and write it all down.

I hear...

....

....

....

....

Repeat the exercise for your other senses.

I smell...

....

....

....

I feel...

....

....

....

I taste...

....

....

....

The regular roar of breaking waves

Wind rushing through long grass

Prickly pine needles

Seaweed drying on the rocks

A fig tree in full sunlight

A warm and powdery top crust of sand

Dried salt puckering the skin around my eyes

Sea salt carried on the air

Pungent campfire smoke

Dawn and dusk

Try writing two poems that describe the same place – but at completely different times of day. Notice how temperatures change, shadows glide and the weather shifts – and people and animals go about their business.

What changes? What doesn't? Who comes and goes? Do you feel differently about the place at different times of day?

A poem is a time machine

You can use your poems to travel back in time. A poem can help you to rediscover things that happened and things you felt in a way that brings the past flickering back to life. On these pages, write a poem that takes you back to a memorable day in your life.

You could write about:

- The day you first met your best friend
- The first time you went really far from home
- How you discovered a hobby you enjoy
- A time you faced one of the things that scares you most

Be sure to use ALL your senses to conjure up the place, time and event you're describing.

Stay focussed

Try to focus on one moment in time. It could be when you realized something:

"And then suddenly I understood that..."

Or met someone:

"She looked over her shoulder at me and said..."

Or did something:

"Then I ducked beneath the breaking wave..."

Stay physical

Use physical details to paint a picture of how you felt at that moment – both inside and out.

- Were the hairs on your arms standing up?

- Could you hear any words at all over the roaring surf?

- Could you smell jasmine flowers on the summer breeze?

More to read

"Adlestrop"
by Edward Thomas

"Those Winter Sundays"
by Robert Hayden

An ode to something great or small

Poems that celebrate a specific person, event or idea are called **odes**. Usually, an ode addresses a great and lofty subject – but poets can also write an ode to something humble and ordinary.

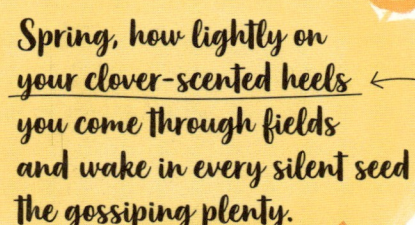

Spring, how lightly on
your clover-scented heels
you come through fields
and wake in every silent seed
the gossiping plenty.

Poets often give personal characteristics to non-human subjects, such as a season or a virtue. This is called **personification**.

When you call out to someone or something directly in a poem – especially when they can't hear you or can't answer back – it's called an **apostrophe**.

Oh goat, you never set your cloven feet
on grass too coarse – or fine – for you to eat.
I wish I could, with such indifference, graze
on meadowsweet and sticks: on blame and praise.

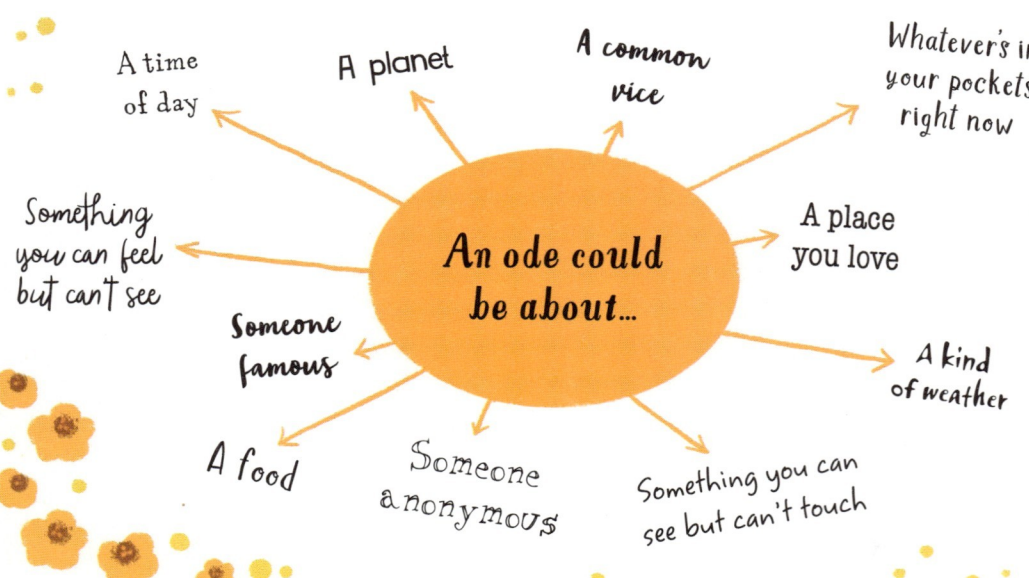

A time of day

A planet

A common vice

Whatever's in your pockets right now

Something you can feel but can't see

An ode could be about...

A place you love

Someone famous

A kind of weather

A food

Someone anonymous

Something you can see but can't touch

Write your own ode here:

Your odes can be long or short, rhyming or unrhymed. In fact, they can be any shape or style you choose.

What makes an ode an ode is the way you speak to and celebrate the subject of your poem.

More to read

"To the Light of September"
by W. S. Merwin

"Ode to my Socks"
by Pablo Neruda

"To the Rain"
by Ursula K. Le Guin

The call of the wild

Try composing a bestiary: a collection of poems about real or imaginary animals. Each poem should describe a single creature – what it looks like, where it lives, what it does. Are there lessons that people could learn from the way this animal behaves?

Richly illustrated bestiaries were popular in Europe during the Middle Ages. They featured ordinary animals – hedgehogs, donkeys and lions – as well as invented ones, such as dragons, unicorns, griffons and basilisks.

More to read

"Spiderweb"
by Kay Ryan

"The Kraken"
by Alfred Lord Tennyson

"Cedar Waxwings Unmasked"
by Jane Yolen

"Marine Display"
by Erica McAlpine

Make your animals as lifelike as possible by describing what they look, sound, feel, smell and – perhaps – even *taste* like.

musty

glittering

stale

fishy

lustrous

glossy

bristly

encrusted

fresh

rasping

charred

bony

slick

woolly

honking

rumbling

spattering

whistling

crunching

slurping

tart

rancid

tangy

nutty

Making art out of art

Write a poem about a work of art that you like. It could be a masterpiece from a museum, or a treasure that nobody seems to notice. You might be inspired by a statue or a painting, a photograph or an ancient pot – any object that someone has made with care.

Questions

- What does the artwork look like?
- What is it made of, and how was it made?
- Does it tell a story?
- What do you know about the person who made it?
- Where did you first spot it?
- What is it used for today?
- How do you feel when you look at it?

More to read

"Fountains of Aix" by May Swenson

"Poem" by Elizabeth Bishop

"An Arundel Tomb" by Philip Larkin

"Why I Am Not a Painter" by Frank O'Hara

Poems that describe works of art are called **ekphrastic** (eck-FRA-stick) poems.

A map to unseen worlds

Draw a map showing a place – either real or imaginary. It could be anywhere: your town, or a tropical island, or a magical forest...

You could draw symbols like these to make a key for your map:

Stream   Mountain   Shipwreck   Quicksand   Fox's den   Iceberg

Now, write a poem describing a journey to a particular place on your map. It could be your house, or a secret hideout, or an enchanted glade. Give lots of details, so that a stranger reading your poem could find the way – *without* needing the map.

Questions

- Is the route easy or difficult to follow?

- What's underfoot? Gravel? Snow? Concrete? Air?

- What obstacles, if any, will a visitor need to overcome?

- Will a visitor coming this way feel cold? Wet? Frightened? Happy?

- Are there passwords or signs that a visitor should know about?

- What will a visitor find at the destination?

More to read

"Directions to My Imaginary Childhood" by Nick Carbó

"Directions" by Billy Collins

"Five Directions to My House" by Juan Felipe Herrera

Don't make a long story short

Some stories are so BIG that you can't write them in a few stanzas or pages. For those, poets reserve a special form: the **epic**. Epics are long, often book-length, poems in which kingdoms rise and fall, gods and humans clash, and civilization hangs in the balance.

What makes an epic an epic?

- It is often set in the distant past, or in a time of magic, myths and legends.

- The action takes place across whole countries and continents and may even extend into the underworld.

- It often features supernatural events and characters – gods, demigods and monsters.

- It includes long speeches and long lists – of ships, for example, or ancestors, or types of flowers.

This book is far too short to contain your epic ambitions, but you can start planning out your own epic poem here:

A hero with a fatal flaw

Epic heroes are larger than life, and may have special powers: superhuman strength, wily intellect, unshakable virtue. But they often have a human weakness or a fatal flaw that means success – and survival – are by no means certain...

Start by creating your own epic hero:

Name:

Description:

Powers:

Flaws:

Invent an impossible task

A great hero needs a desperate mission or an unbeatable foe. What will your hero need to accomplish? Will she face a troll whose gold left eye can see one minute into the future? Can he stop the asteroid hurtling towards Earth? Will they rescue their best friend from the underworld?

Give your hero some obstacles to overcome – and one *seemingly* impossible task:

1. _____

_____

_____

2. _____

_____

_____

3. _____

_____

_____

4. _____

_____

_____

Feats of memory

Historians think that many of the oldest epic poems were composed long before they were written down at all.

Poets memorized thousands of lines of poetry, and then recited them at banquets and festivals to entertain people. Only much later were they recorded in books.

More to read

"Beowulf" by Anonymous

"The Aeneid" by Virgil

"Omeros" by Derek Walcott

Help is on its way

Many heroes would fail immediately if not for trusted allies,
sound advice or a little magical aid. Who will assist your hero?
A talking sparrow? A surly garden gnome? A rival turned best friend?

Once upon a time, in a land far away...

Where will the events in your story take place? And when?
Use this space to describe the world of your poem – or to draw a map.

Start in the middle

Now you're ready to start. But epic poems don't usually start at the very beginning of the story. They plunge right into the heart of the action, and fill in any gaps with flashbacks.

Write the first scene of your epic poem here:

_____

_____

_____

_____

_____

_____

_____

_____

_____

_____

_____

_____

_____

_____

_____

_____

_____

_____

Interlocking rhymes

Your epic can have any rhythm and rhyme scheme you like...

...but you *could* try writing it using something called **terza rima**. This is a chain of rhymes that you can make as long as you like:

aba bcb cdc ded efe...

To end the poem, just close it with a rhyming couplet – two lines that rhyme with each other:

...wxw xyx yzy zz

This rhyming pattern was made popular by an Italian poet from medieval times named Dante Alighieri, who wrote a famous epic poem called **The Divine Comedy**.

Pushing the boundaries

Do poems have to make sense? Is it ok just to make up words? Is rapping poetry?

In this section, you can try all kinds of offbeat and experimental poetry styles – from cut-and-paste collage (what's that!?) to haiku collaborations.

Stop making sense

One of the great things about poetry is that you can enjoy it, even when it hardly makes sense at all. This is especially true in **nonsense poems**: silly, light-hearted poems that play fast and loose with the rules of language and logic.

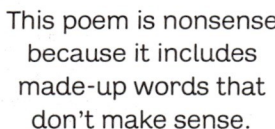

chirrup

I heard the mournful chirrup of the snail;
I combed the curly whiskers of the whale;
I counted flocks of tigers by their fins
and stroked the purring jellyfishes' chins.

This poem is nonsense. How can a snail chirrup or jellyfish have chins?

Who garps in the glow of the climpering Moon,
that frapples the bixen so long into June?
Who treads in the fooshplats the bixen bestrew?
Oh foosh-footed brango, say, might it be you?

This poem is nonsense because it includes made-up words that don't make sense.

Fabricoct a converjam

Don't hesitate to make up a word, if the word you want doesn't exist – yet. One way to do this is to make a **portmanteau**. Based on the French word for *suitcase*, this term describes a new word made by jamming together two old words.

For example:

- Breakfast + lunch = **brunch**
- Motor + hotel = **motel**
- Smoke + fog = **smog**
- Fabricate + concoct = **fabricoct**
- Conversation + jam = **converjam**

Try inventing some new words to use in your poems here:

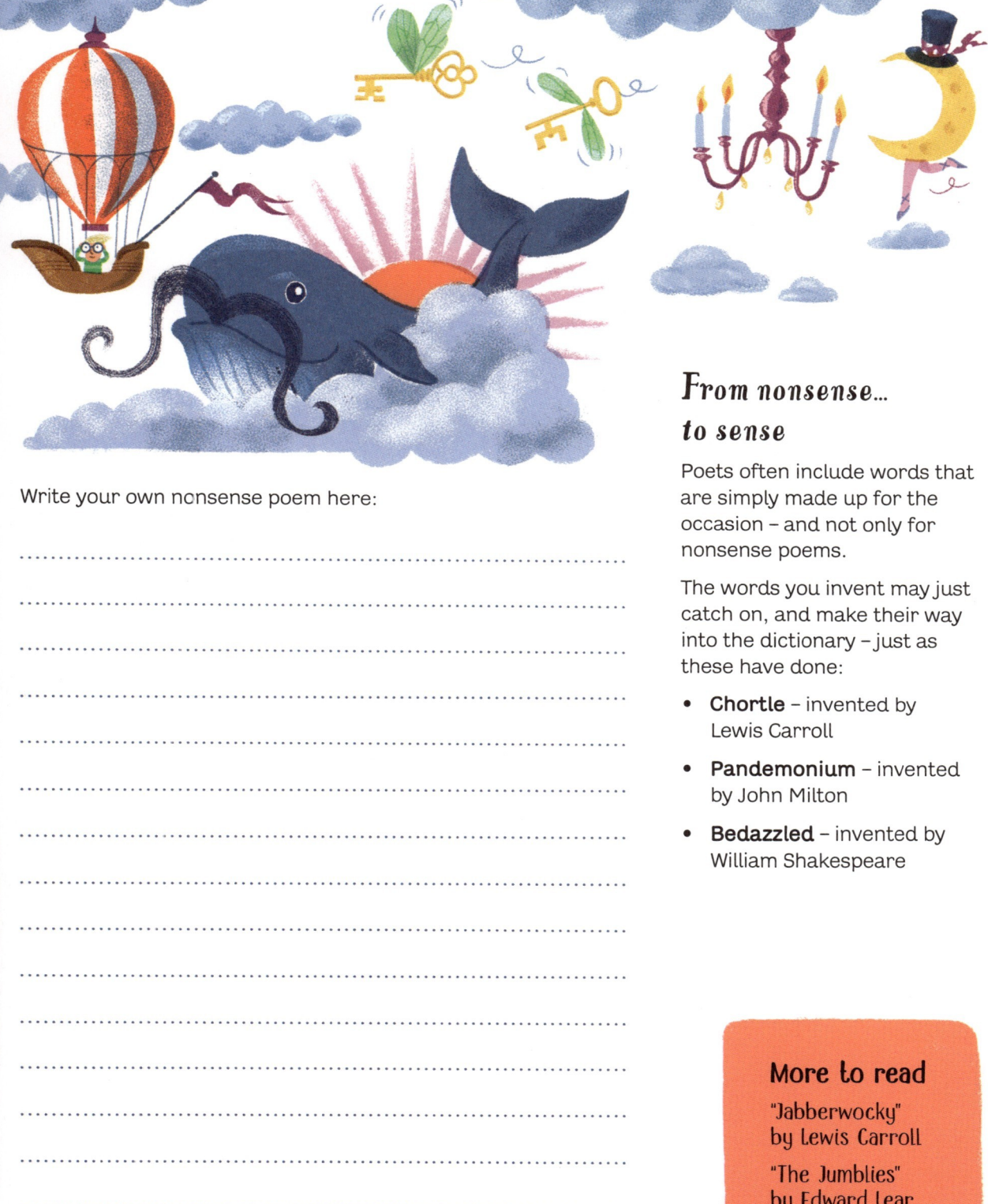

Write your own nonsense poem here:

....
....
....
....
....
....
....
....
....
....
....
....
....
....
....
....

From nonsense... to sense

Poets often include words that are simply made up for the occasion – and not only for nonsense poems.

The words you invent may just catch on, and make their way into the dictionary – just as these have done:

- **Chortle** – invented by Lewis Carroll

- **Pandemonium** – invented by John Milton

- **Bedazzled** – invented by William Shakespeare

More to read

"Jabberwocky" by Lewis Carroll

"The Jumblies" by Edward Lear

Erasing a poem

You can write poetry without writing anything at all. Copy a page of text – a poem, a page from a novel or an article from a newspaper. Then, use a thick black pen, or splotches of paint, to blot or scribble over chunks of text, leaving behind a completely new poem. This is what's known as **erasure** or **blackout poetry**.

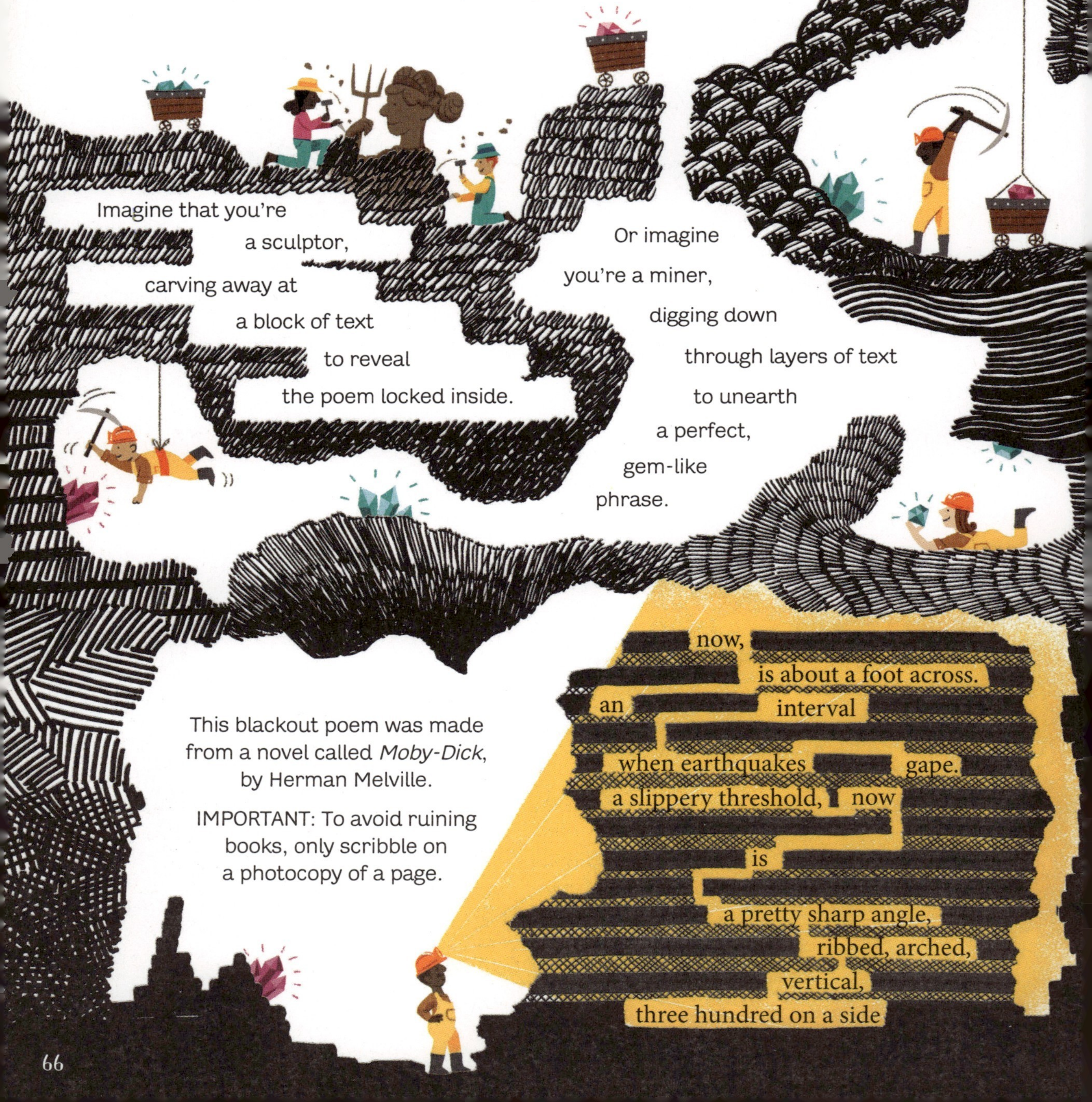

Imagine that you're
a sculptor,
carving away at
a block of text
to reveal
the poem locked inside.

Or imagine
you're a miner,
digging down
through layers of text
to unearth
a perfect,
gem-like
phrase.

This blackout poem was made from a novel called *Moby-Dick*, by Herman Melville.

IMPORTANT: To avoid ruining books, only scribble on a photocopy of a page.

now,
is about a foot across.
an   interval
when earthquakes   gape.
a slippery threshold,   now
is
a pretty sharp angle,
ribbed, arched,
vertical,
three hundred on a side

Paste your own blackout poem here:

Snip, rip, copy, glue

Sometimes, poets put down their pens and pick up scissors instead. Just as artists snip out bright shapes and patterns to assemble into a collage, you can take whole lines from other poems to create something new.

Poems made up using lines from other poems are called **cento poems** or **collage poems**.

The Seafarer

Teach me to hear mermaids singing,
That lift the deep upon their backs,
That in the murk and tongueless night
Do what the panther dare not.

Let me combine
The Milky Way, the bird of Paradise
To see both blended in one flood
Of balm, of oil, of spice, of ambergris.

Ask me no more if east or west
I'll go, and, by thy kind leave, leave behind.
In this strange labyrinth how shall I turn –
Which is the Mermaid's now, but shall be mine?

The lines in this new cento poem come from these poets, who lived hundreds of years ago: John Donne, Andrew Marvell, Robert Herrick, Anonymous, George Herbert, George Herbert, Richard Crashaw, Robert Herrick, Thomas Carew, John Donne, Mary Wroth, Ben Jonson.

More to read

"The Dong with the Luminous Nose" by John Ashbery

Create your own collage poem here. You could copy
out lines from books of poetry – or, if you prefer,
cut out phrases and words from old magazines
and newspapers to stick on the page.

Tips

Try to use lines from lots of different
sources – not just a single poem or book.

Choose from poems on different
subjects and in different styles.

It may help to start by reading lots of poems and jotting
down lines you think are strange or interesting.

Don't feel your poem has to make perfect sense,
or be perfectly grammatical. Let it be a little weird.

Poems off the page

You don't always need a pen
or paper to write a poem...

Evaporating poems

Fill a glass with water and go
outdoors. Use your fingers or
a large brush to paint words
on footpaths or driveways.

(Make sure you aren't
in the way of any
people or cars!)

Seaside sonnets

Use a stick – or your finger –
to write in the wet sand on a beach.
See if you can write a whole poem
before the waves wash it away.

Rhyming on the move

Go for a long walk. Make up a line of poetry, and recite it
until you know it by heart. Then add another line, and
another – repeating your whole poem as you go
to make sure your remember it all.

In the early 1900s, explorers on long Arctic
treks often made up funny, rhyming verses
while hauling their sleds across the ice.
These "sledging songs" helped them keep
a steady pace, and distracted them from
their cold feet and weary backs.

Chance operations

Some poems leave everything up to chance. On this page, write a poem using just a book (any book) and a pack of playing cards.

Poems such as these are called **chance operations**.

Here's how:

1. Open a book to any page – but preferably one with lots of text. The words of your poem will come from this page.

2. Shuffle your cards. Then, to write a five-line poem, turn over five cards at random.

3. Each card will tell you how many words to copy, and from which line of the page:

Diamonds = 3 words	A = 1	6 = 6	J = 11
Clubs = 4 words	2 = 2	7 = 7	Q = 12
Hearts = 5 words	3 = 3	8 = 8	K = 13
Spades = 6 words	4 = 4	9 = 9	
	5 = 5	10 = 10	

They won't always make sense...

...but try writing a lot of them, and then copy the two you like best below.

So, for example, if you drew these five cards:

The first line of your poem would be the first *four* words from the *fifth* line on the page.

The last line of your poem would be the first *five* words from the *twelfth* line on the page.

4. Ignore punctuation. Keep an ace up your sleeve. **Cheat as much as you like.**

_____   _____

_____   _____

_____   _____

_____   _____

_____   _____

Poetry out loud

For as long as poetry has existed, it has existed out loud. People were reciting, singing and performing their poems to audiences long before pens, paper and writing were even invented.

Boisterous ballads

For centuries, people have told popular tales of love, crime and woe in the form of **ballads**: rhyming poems that were usually sung, not read.

> My true love planted apple trees   a
> before she went to sea.   b
> The boughs dip low with golden fruit   c
> That tastes of brine to me.   b

A ballad stanza is typically four lines long, and rhymes in an abcb pattern.

Write your own ballad here:

_____

_____

_____

_____

_____

_____

_____

_____

_____

_____

_____

_____

Singing the blues

The **blues** is a kind of music and poetry invented by African Americans. Blues lyrics traditionally reflect on poverty and heartbreak – but they often include wry comedy, and rely on repetitions to spin out a story slowly.

I get up early every morning, long before the Sun comes up.
I get up early every morning, and I watch that Sun come up.
I got nothing but a dew drop down inside my coffee cup.

In many traditional blues poems, the second line echoes the first.

The third line rhymes with the first two.

Write your own blues poem here:

_____

_____

_____

_____

_____

_____

_____

_____

_____

_____

_____

_____

_____

_____

_____

More to read

"Po' Boy Blues"
by Langston Hughes

"Riverbank Blues"
by Sterling A. Brown

More to listen to

"The Banks of the Ohio"
by Anonymous

"Barbara Allen"
by Anonymous

"Levee Camp Blues"
by Son House

"I Ain't Superstitious"
by Howlin' Wolf

Straight outta Greenland

Many poems being written today come in the form of **rap** or **hip-hop** – an art form in which people speak rhythmically over music. With fast-flowing rhymes, complex rhythms and wide-ranging vocabularies, rappers are constantly inventing new types of poetry.

This rapping narwhal (scientific name: *Monodon monoceros*) is performing a verse in lines or "bars" of four beats each. The stars mark the syllable where the beat lands.

People call me monoceros, or "single horn" –

But despite the pointy profile I'm no unicorn.

I've got a tusk that's a tooth with a helical twist –

I'm dropping mythical flows that you can't dismiss.

I'm a narwhal – yeah, don't look so surprised.

A lot of us whales can vocalize.

You didn't think that a cetacean could be rocking the joint?

You didn't think that my creations could be so on point?

Well peace, love and halibut – that's my credo.

Living underwater it's the only way to be, though:

Taking it slow, just a breath at a time,

And for every breath I take I make a brand new rhyme.

Hey, *helical* is a word that means *turning in a spiral*.

Oh – that makes sense. And *cetacean* (seh-TAY-shun) is a scientific word that describes whales, dolphins and porpoises.

A *credo* is like a personal motto... Yo, he's got the beats AND the vocab!

Try writing your own rap here. Remember to rap out loud as you go, so that you can hear how the rhythms and rhymes flow together.

You might want to add in marks to show where the beats go in each bar.

Let the streets in

One of the great things about hip-hop is that rappers often include local slang and jargon in their poetry.

Rap is a particularly good place to let your own dialect, accent and vocabulary come into your writing. These all help to make your voice unique.

Team efforts

You don't have to go it alone.
Writing poetry can be a team effort.

Hold a poetry party

For centuries, Japanese poets have held parties outdoors, where they can write surrounded by nature. Together, they improvise long, interlinking chains of poetry called **haikai no renga**.

*Stags leaping fences;
the Milky Way arches up,
sucks in its tummy.*

*So: even our swift, small lives
can prickle infinity.*

*Through wet, pink petals
steady trails of ants depart
the abbot's picnic.*

*All have an eye for beauty:
rising moon or bowl of rice.*

1. Someone composes a haiku: three lines adding up to a total of 17 syllables.*

2. Another poet adds a **couplet**, or pair of lines, each seven syllables long, which combine with the haiku to create a five-line mini-poem within the longer chain.

3. A third poet writes a haiku which, linked with the preceding couplet, forms a new mini-poem.

4. Alternating between haikus and couplets, the poets make a chain of poems that can turn and skip from one subject to another.

Write your own haiku here to add to the chain.

*For more on haikus, see page 10.

Create an exquisite corpse

In the 1920s, French writers and intellectuals gathered in cafés, where they invented a group poem called an **exquisite corpse**. It requires writers to add lines to a poem without knowing what has come before. Here's how it works:

1. Sabine writes the first three lines of a poem, then folds the page to hide the two opening lines.

2. Pierre adds three new lines to the poem. Then, he folds the page again, hiding all but the last line.

3. Other poets join in – or Sabine and Pierre take turns – until they fill the page and unfold it to read aloud.

You gave a look like a labrador
deciding no one
licks a bullfrog more than twice.
Slugs and snails are another story.
I once kissed a snail so pretty
a second kiss seemed obligatory.
Isn't most of love the circling back
and snuffling near to what you could
but will not any longer do without?
Now, I could imagine not at all,
ever, licking an elephant.
They're simply too big and too tall.

The finished poem is often a patchwork of different styles, images and ideas.

You could make an exquisite corpse using pictures instead of words.

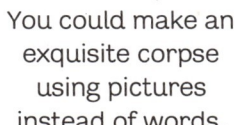

Get in line

Write some poems on these pages. Let the lengths and shapes of the lines guide you, interrupt you or lead you astray. Let your poems overlap and influence one another.

1. Write a short poem below, on any subject, using long lines.

2. Now write out the same poem again, this time breaking the lines so that each is just a few words long.

3. How has changing the line lengths changed your poem? Does it feel faster? Slower? Louder? Quieter? Do different words stand out? Which version do you like best?

Toolkit

What do you call a line that goes **da DUM, da DUM, da DUM, da DUM**? What can you do to become a better poet? What should you do if you've run out of ideas?

In this section, you'll find all the useful tools you need to keep writing amazing poems.

What is poetry?

Now that you've written lots of poems of your own, you can help tackle this age-old question. Lots of people have *some* ideas about what poetry can be... but the truth is, *nobody* has a final answer. Poetry can be *many* things – and poets like you are always writing new poems and inventing new kinds of poetry.

Fill in the blanks in these bubbles with your own ideas.

A way of discovering what you mean to say

A word game without any rules

An answer to questions you can't answer any other way

A way of saying what you'd *never* say otherwise

A poem is...

A snapshot of what's on your mind

A kind of music made of words

A message in a bottle

Fearless

Lucky

Silly

Inspired

Stubborn

Honest

Stylish

A poet should be...

Instinctive

Angry

Patient

Idle

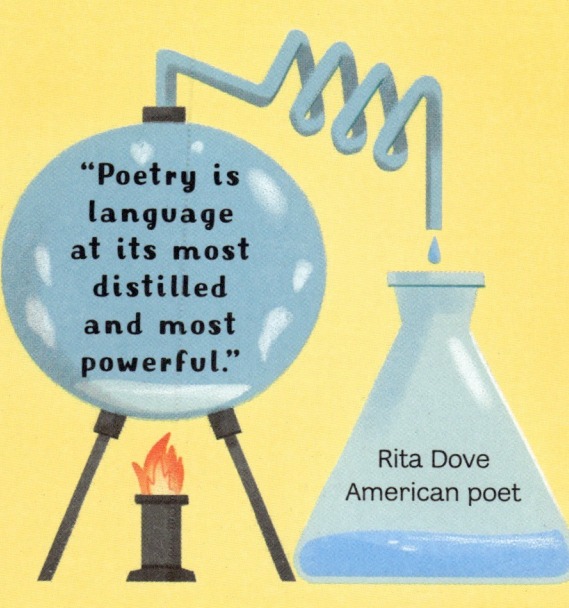

"Poetry is language at its most distilled and most powerful."

Rita Dove
American poet

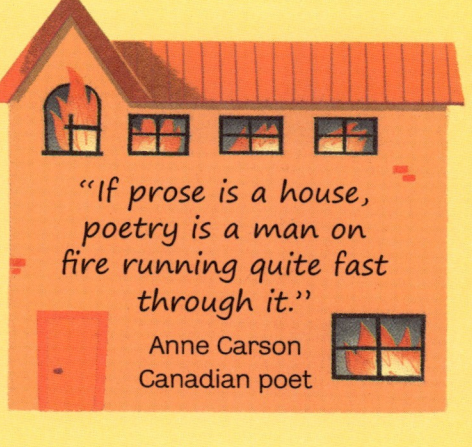

"If prose is a house, poetry is a man on fire running quite fast through it."

Anne Carson
Canadian poet

"The fate of poetry is to fall in love with the world."

Derek Walcott
Saint Lucian poet

Poems about poetry

Poems that try to explain what poetry is, what it's for, and how it should be written are called **ars poetica**. This means the **art of poetry** in Latin.

Write your own ars poetica here:

What makes a poem a poem?

In this book, you've encountered many of the different elements that help to make poems *look*, *feel* and *sound* like poems. Here is a summary of some of them:

Line: Most poems are divided into lines, which can be of any length.

Title: This can be read either as a description of the poem, or part of it.

Line break: The point at which a line "breaks" or ends.

To the dwarf planet Pluto*

You're unlike the other planets.
Dimmer, farther, darker, and it
seems your crust is ice, not granite –
airless gases lightly fan it.

Actually, you're NOT a planet:
pip among the pomegranates,
you're too small. You've been rebranded.
A dwarf can't just re-planet. Can it?

Stanza: A group of lines within a poem.

Stanza break: The gap separating one stanza from another.

End-stop and enjambment: If a line ends with punctuation, it is **end-stopped**. If a line carries straight on over the line break, as it does here, it is **enjambed**.

End-rhymes: Rhymes that come at the end of a line.

Slant rhyme: A rhyme that doesn't rhyme perfectly – that sounds just a little off.

Internal rhyme: A rhyme that occurs within a single line.

Rhyme scheme: The pattern of rhymes found in a particular stanza or poem. In this case, every end-rhyme is the same. This is called **monorhyme**.

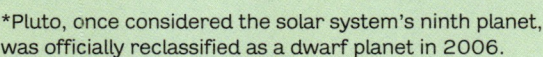

*Pluto, once considered the solar system's ninth planet, was officially reclassified as a dwarf planet in 2006.

Sounds to startle and delight

There are lots of ways you can use the sound of words, as well as their meaning, to make your poems beautiful, interesting and memorable.

Alliteration
The repetition of consonant sounds

Ice-encircled Saturn seems to soar along its orbit.

Venus, veiled in acids, vainly gleams upon the night.

Assonance
The repetition of vowel sounds

Mars this morning seems to have been dreaming in the sky.

What Neptune's moons do in the gloom it is too soon to say.

Onomotopoeia
(on-oh-mah-toe-PEA-ah) Words that sound like the noises or actions they describe

Zip   Crunch   Whoosh   Crackle   Fizzle

Hush   Crash   Zap

Boom   Splash   Slam

These words can make you feel as though you're actually hearing the thing they describe.

Regular rhythms

Many poems are written so that the rhythms of the words fall into a repeating pattern. This kind of poetry is called **metrical**. In English, the syllables of a word can be either **stressed** or **unstressed**. You can usually find out which by saying them out loud:

The pla net I like best is Earth.
da DUM da DUM da DUM da DUM

— Stressed
— Unstressed

This pattern, where the unstressed syllable comes first, is very common, and is called **iambic** (eye-AM-bick).

This pattern, where the stressed syllable comes first, is called **trochaic** (troh-KAY-ick).

Pla nets bore me – moons are bet ter.
DUM da DUM da DUM da DUM da

You can use other, more complex patterns in metrical poetry. This one is called **dactyllic** (dack-TILL-ick).

Big ger than all oth er pla nets is Ju pi ter!
DUM da da DUM da da DUM da da DUM da da

Tantalizing titles

A title can be a useful starting point to inspire and give direction to your writing. It can be a spark that starts a fire, a key to crack enigmas with, or a question only your new poem can answer.

Here is a list of made-up titles. Try writing some more of your own. Don't worry about the poems themselves – just focus on what makes each title intriguing or exciting.

THE CAPTIVES

Spoken at Dawn Among Sand Dunes

For a Hibernating Dormouse

The Alligator Pear

Fifty Names I Never Speak

Clip Clop Clippity Clop

A Prickle, Numbness, then a Pain

What the Tiger Said

Made With Love By Robots

Poem Composed While Holding My Breath

The Pre-flight Check

An Invitation

Poem in the Shape of a Sea Snail

Choose the title from the page opposite that most inspires you, and use this space to write a poem to pair with it. You could look back through this book for help choosing a style or form of poem to suit your title.

Poems with great titles

"Thirteen Ways of Looking at a Blackbird"
by Wallace Stevens

"I Was Sleeping Where the Black Oaks Move"
by Louise Erdrich

"Diving into the Wreck"
by Adrienne Rich

"What My House Would Be Like If It Were A Person"
by Denise Levertov

Common types of titles

- A time and place
- A question
- A quotation
- A phrase in a foreign language
- A dedication
- A state of mind
- The object your poem might describe
- The first words of your poem
- The last words of your poem
- The name of the character speaking your poem

If you're ever suffering from writer's block, or want to try something new and different, select a title from your list – and away you go!

Almost every new poem can be improved, and most great poems have been revised again and again.

You may be able to fix a poem with a few small changes – but if not, here are some more radical strategies.

Start here by copying out a poem that you've already written. Use one or more of the strategies on these pages to transform and improve it. Then, write your revised poem on the page opposite.

Start here:

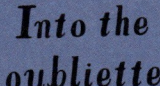

Into the oubliette

An oubliette is a tiny dungeon where medieval rulers once put prisoners to be forgotten.

Try tossing your poem into an oubliette. Leave it in a notebook – out of sight – and forget about it, for as long as a week.

Then come back to the poem with fresh eyes. Do you like it more or less than before? Which lines work? Which don't? Rewrite accordingly.

"My pencils outlast their erasers."
–Vladimir Nabokov
(Russian writer, 1899-1977)

Just one good line

Often, an early version of a poem is a mixture of good and bad. Identify the very best line in your poem. Cut the rest.

Make this the first line of your revised poem and rewrite the rest from scratch.

. . . .

. . . .

. . . .

. . . .

. . . .

. . . .

. . . .

. . . .

Finish here:

Upside down and opposite

If your poem isn't working and it's got you stumped, try putting your last line first. Start the story from the ending.

Or try saying the opposite of what you meant to say. Turn a poem about the past into a poem about the future. Change night into day, me into you, yes into no.

You may surprise yourself by writing something stranger and truer than you intended.

How do you know when a poem is finished?

- When changing any one word makes it worse.
- When you think the poem has earned all its faults.
- "A poem is never finished; it is only abandoned."
  –Paul Valéry (French writer, 1871-1945)

"I believe more in the scissors than I do in the pencil."
–Truman Capote (American writer, 1924-1984)

Snip, tear, shuffle

1. Sometimes all the elements of your poem are there on the page – but they're just not in the right order.

2. Copy your poem onto a fresh sheet of paper – then cut or tear it into fragments or stanzas or even individual lines.

3. Then, mix them up. Try out various combinations and arrangements.

4. Do some parts work better together? Does a new order create a sharper, brighter poem? Is every piece necessary?

5. Create a new poem from the scraps of the old one.

Invent a secret identity

Sometimes, people want to share their poems, but they don't want everyone to know who wrote them. To keep their identity a secret, they use a **nom de plume** – which means "pen name" in French.

Why so secret?

People often write things in poetry that are hard to talk about in real life. Using a nom de plume can make you feel freer to write about yourself – or to try wild poetry experiments – without worrying about what others might think of you.

Famous pen names

- **Mark Twain** was the pen name of Samuel Clemens. It was a phrase used by steamboat sailors on the Mississippi river.

- A French diplomat named Alexis Leger used the pen name **Saint-John Perse**. He didn't want to mix his professional and his poetic identities.

- English novelist Mary Ann Evans used the name **George Eliot** when she published her work.

PLUMINATOR 3,000

Invent your own pen names using this contraption.

1. Fill in the blanks in each column.
(There are some examples given here to help you.)

Column A	Column B
Month (*such as November*)	Famous battle (*such as Waterloo*)
Name of an island (*St. Helena*)	Musical instrument (*Ocarina*)
Useful virtue (*Patience*)	Any nationality (*Senegalese*)
Mythical character (*Perseus*)	Name of a river (*Orinoco*)
Grandmother's name (*Barbara*)	Mode of transport (*Barge*)

2. Now try pairing words from the two columns until you get a combination that you like.

3. You are: Helena Waterloo
Perseus Barge

Everyday tips for poets

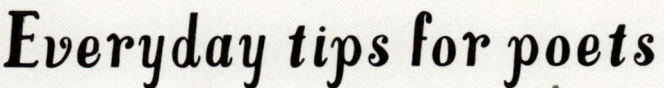

Everyday means every single day

Write at least one new line of poetry every day. Regular practice will make you a better, sharper, stronger writer.

Read, read, read

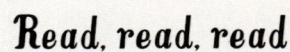

Read as much poetry as you can: old and new, strange and familiar. This is a way to find inspiration, to steal ideas, to learn what you like, to choose what you do (and don't) want to write yourself.

Make a mood board

Bring together drawings and photographs that inspire you, along with quotations, scraps of poetry and found objects such as leaves or seashells – anything that puts you in the right mood for writing.

Use the WHOLE dictionary

Phalanx. Arduous. Rosin. Zastrugi. There are more than a quarter of a million words in the English language, and they are *all* available to you. Use a notebook to keep a running list of new, strange and interesting words to add to your poems.

Keep a journal

Write down thoughts, dreams and events from your daily life. Keep notes on places you go and people you meet. In time, all of this could find its way into a poem.

Write out loud

Speak your poems out loud as you write them. This will help you test out the sound of your lines – the rhythms and rhymes – as well as their meaning. Poetry can be a kind of music, and your voice is your instrument.

Learn some poems by heart

When you learn every word of a poem, you discover things you could never know just from reading it. And what's more, a poem you know by heart can stay with you – a faithful companion – forever.

Poetry first aid

At some point, you may find yourself stuck in a rut, stumped by a difficult poem or running out of ideas. Never fear: it happens to everyone – and this poetry first-aid kit is here to help.

Get on your walking shoes

Get up, get out, get away from your poem. Go outside, do a handstand or hold a yoga pose. Fresh air and physical activity are a great way to shake loose new ideas.

Try new tools for a new sound

Change your writing tools. If you're used to writing with a pen, try writing with a crayon. If you usually write in a little notebook, try scrawling on a huge sheet of drawing paper.

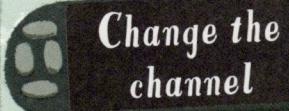
Change the channel

Has your epic poem ground to a halt? Spend an afternoon writing limericks. Are your triolets feeling tired? Let loose with a prose poem.

Borrow inspiration

You can always borrow inspiration from another art form. Look at paintings in a museum, or listen to music you've never heard before, or teach yourself a new dance move.

Emergency measures

If you're experiencing a really serious case of writer's block, just try one of these emergency writing exercises to get yourself going again.

Free writing

Find a clock or watch so you can time yourself. For five minutes, scribble whatever words come into your head: meaningful, meaningless, bonkers or repetitive – don't worry about how they go together.

When you finish, pick out the best lines. Use them to create a new poem.

Steal something you love

Choose one great line from a famous poem you really love. Steal it, and make it into the first line of a new poem of your own.

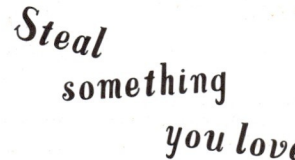

Crossword puzzle

Try writing a poem in the form of crossword puzzle clues. It could be divided into two parts: one called **Across**, and one called **Down**.

Anaphora experiment

Write a poem in which every line begins with exactly the same word or phrase. This is an ancient literary trick called **anaphora**.

You could choose one of these:

Until…

Without…

Because…

Predict the future

Write a poem that describes, in detail, events taking place far in the future. You could compose an invitation for your 90th birthday party – or a prophecy of the End of the World.

Acknowledgements

Poetry tips and sample poems by Jerome Martin

Illustrated by Marco Bonatti and Toby Newsome

Designed by Tabitha Blore, Laura Wood and Lucy Wain

Cover illustration by El Primo Ramon

Edited by Ruth Brocklehurst

Poetry expert: Dr. Erica McAlpine,

St Edmund Hall, University of Oxford